**AN UNOFFICIAL GRAPHIC NOVEL
FOR MINECRAFTERS**

The ENDER EYE PROPHECY

CARA J. STEVENS

ART BY **DAVID NORGREN**
AND **ELIAS NORGREN**

SCHOLASTIC INC.

Special thanks to Cara J. Stevens, David Norgren, and Elias Norgren

ISBN 978-1-338-16978-2

12 11 10 9 8 7 6 5 4 3 2 1   17 18 19 20 21 22

Printed in the U.S.A.   40

First Scholastic printing, January 2017

Cover design by Brian Peterson
Cover illustration credit Bethany Straker
Editor: Rachel Stark
Designer: Joshua Barnaby

INTRODUCTION

If you have played Minecraft, then you know all about Minecraft worlds. They're made of blocks you can mine: coal, dirt, and sand. In the game, you'll find many different creatures, lands, and villages inhabited by strange villagers with bald heads. The villagers who live there have their own special, magical worlds that are protected by a string of border worlds to stop outsiders from finding them.

When we last left off on the small border world of Xenos, Phoenix was looking for a way to safely return home to her parents and brother. Unfortunately, the dangers she and T.H. had faced when curing the zombie monks still loomed large. What's more, the village in which Phoenix grew up still refused to allow her, a miner, inside its walls.

Our story resumes as T.H. and Phoenix are getting restless, waiting for their next adventure to begin.

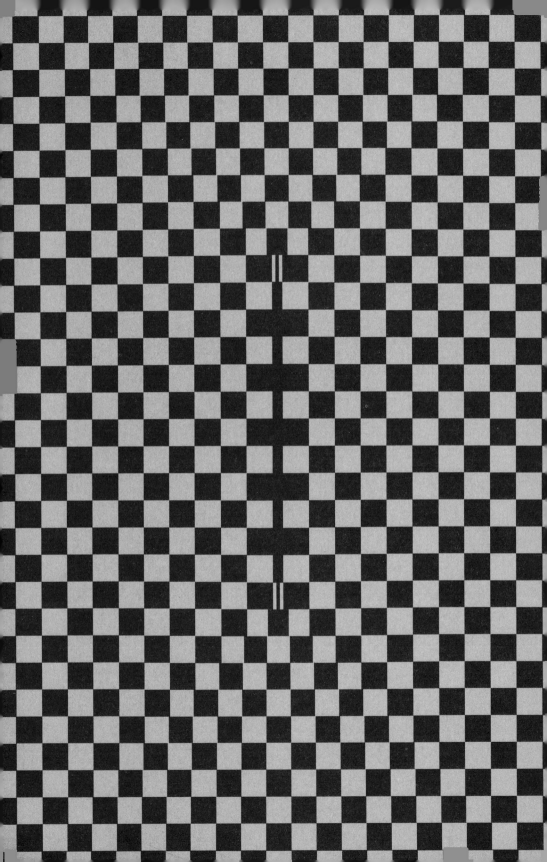

CHAPTER 1

THE BAD SEED

≷Cluck!≷

≷sigh≷
Back to the
daily chores.

I almost miss
fighting zombies and
running from bad guys.

Do you ever get to go to those worlds?

Wait. Can *I* go to one of those worlds?

Only Pollinators get to jump worlds...

Oh.

You are brave and strong and smart, Phoenix. You could be an excellent Pollinator some day. If that's what you want to be.

Some are really neat.

Remember the Defender?

You mean the guy who sent hostile mobs to attack us and turned your parents into zombies? That Defender?

Yep, that guy. He kinda, um, spawned from a world we pollinated.

We didn't realize there was a bad seed. The Defender was a glitch.

Even though he is gone, exiled to the Far Lands, more hostile mobs could come from the same seed world, unless we destroy it.

So now it's our responsibility to flip the switch to turn it off.

You're going, too?

Pumpkinhead's first mission, too!

Yep! It's my first mission.

Cheer up, Phoenix. They won't be gone long.

I hate getting left behind, Wolfie. I miss having adventures.

Be careful what you wish for, Phoenix.

Come on, Phoenix! Let's play tag. You're it!

≒HUMPH!≒

≒CLUCK!≒

Not now, Wolfie.

CHAPTER 2

THE PROPHECY

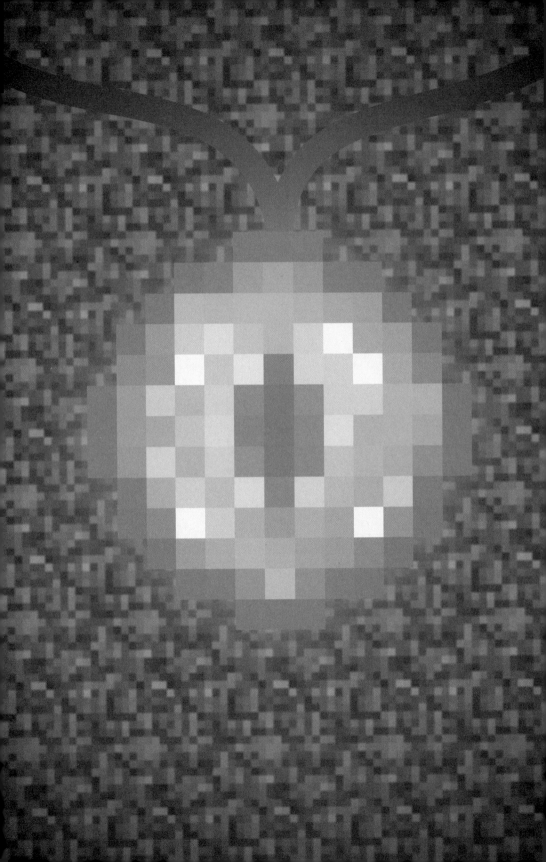

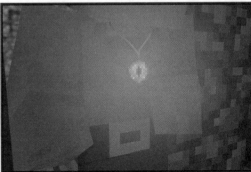

Um, I think you have the wrong house.

I assure you we are in the right place. You wear the enchanted Eye of Ender.

This is just a necklace my parents gave me.

Hey, Phoenix. These guys smell good. I think they're honest.

Our trouble with the Defender taught me not to trust people too quickly. I'll hear what they have to say before I decide.

I'm not sure I should trust you.

She is smart.

She is just as the prophecy describes her.

Well, Phoenix or Violet, either way, you are more important than you realize.

But I'm just a kid. What can I do?

The prophecy says you can save our world.

Haven't you ever felt it?

Felt what, exactly?

Different from everyone else. Like you're meant for bigger things.

All the time, actually.

I grew up feeling like I was different. I mean, I look different...but that isn't it.

While everyone else was happy reading and living a quiet life, I wanted to get out and explore.

But honestly, I don't believe in prophecies. And I don't believe I'm more special than anyone else. I'm just a kid who feels different.

You're not just a kid. You're a kid with an enchanted necklace.

I just have to leave a note...

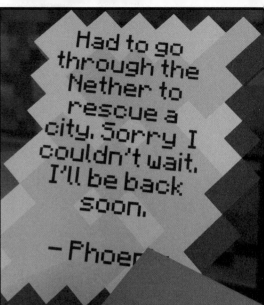

Had to go through the Nether to rescue a city. Sorry I couldn't wait. I'll be back soon.

– Phoer

Okay, Wolfie, give this to T.H. and his parents when they get back.

Be good! I'll be back soon!

I'll stay here and tell those guys what happened. Go be a sneaky little kitty and see where they're taking her.

CHAPTER 3

BACK TO
BUSINESS

Scary cave.

You keep any snacks in here?

Sorry, Tom. All I have is this apple.

Mooooom!

≥sigh≤ Okay, T.H. Here's your apple.

≥Nom nom nom≤ Thanks Mom!

Come on. Let's do this and get out of here.

This cave always gives me the willies.

I thought you loved doing this stuff.

It's exciting work, but pollinating can get pretty dangerous.

Well, we're here.

Wear this. The boots will soften your landing, and the rest will protect you.

I'm afraid to ask what it'll protect me from.

Where my armor?

You won't need it, my sturdy friend.

No Ender pearl! Pearl make golem angry.

Don't worry, Pumpkinhead. I'll throw it in this hole, so you won't have to see it.

Everybody ready?

AAAAHHHHHHH

CHAPTER 4

INTO THE NETHER

But what is it? And who lives there? And can we visit it on the way back?

One: It's a Nether fortress. Two: Angry blazes live there. Three: No, we cannot. We have to keep you safe.

Cool! What's that?

You've never seen a giant lava pit before?

I've practically never seen anything before. This is my first trip to the Nether.

If Concordia is in the Overworld, why are we traveling through the Nether to get there?

We can travel eight times faster down here. There's a portal just a day's journey away that takes us back up to Concordia.

Okay,
I can handle this.
I'm a little freaked out,
but it's an adventure and
I can totally do this!

So we need to at
least give you weapons.
Ones you won't hurt
yourself with.

Weapons?
Oh my!

Maybe
a bow for
Squig...

...and a shield
for Len.

Everyone
ready?

Those were magma cubes. Cute, but dangerous. Lucky I was there with my bow and arrow!

That is what the Luck Enchantment was for.

Luck had nothing to do with it. Our enchantment ran out a few minutes ago. I'm just a good shot!

Stop gathering and start moving, Squig. We came to the Nether to SAVE time, remember?

This soul sand will be useful later, I'm sure.

All right, all right. Hold your horses, Len.

You hold your horses, Squig. I'll ride mine.

You're a funny guy, Len.

RUMBLE

GROAN

RUMBLE

GROAN

Peace isn't good business for everyone, Len. It isn't good business for fixers like me.

There she is, boys. Get her! And get those ridiculous messengers, too.

With you meddling folks out of the picture, I can keep stirring things up in Concordia while I pretend to fix them.

You won't get away with this, Toby.

But I already have. Told them I was coming to protect the girl. You useless miners have no combat training. The Nether is a dangerous place, after all.

CHAPTER 5

GONE

PHOENIX! I'm back! It was so cool!

It was awesome! And scary. But mostly awesome.

But also scary...

Phoenix?

Um, yeah. About Phoenix.

She, um, left with these two guys...

Okay, tell me everything that happened since we left. Don't leave anything out.

30 minutes later...

We're off to see Phoenix's family. We have to let them know what happened. Maybe they'll have some clues.

Be careful. That village doesn't take too kindly to visitors.

This is going to be tough, but it's the only way in.

Dad?

⸘Sniff, sniff⸘

Sit. You can eat while we talk.

I am a little hungry.

Good. Children should be hungry. So why are we worried about our friend Phoenix? Tell me everything.

≥Nom nom nom≤

It all started with Phoenix's necklace.

Some time later...

≥Nom nom nom≤

...and now she is somewhere in the Nether with two strangers.

Ah. And so it begins.

Stay here. Don't open the door for anyone. I'll be right back.

Where do you think she's going?

Hopefully to get Phoenix's parents.

Now the whole family's here.

Is this the hermit who helped save me when I was a zombie?

Um, yeah. Hi Xander. i'm Tom. I mean, T.H.

Ah, I knew you looked familiar.

CHAPTER 6

A RIVER OF LAVA

Oooooohhhhhhh!

Oooooohhhhhhh!

Oooooohhhhhhh!

Oooooohhhhhhh!

Even without my necklace, which your captain will never figure out, I have many special powers.

But Miss Phoenix. Your necklace doesn't w--

Miss Phoenix, be careful. Your powers are too strong for this small ship

No, Len. Let's not reveal all of our Prophetess's secrets to our zombie pigman friends...

Please do be careful with your magic. This ship has been in my family for many years.

We do need to please our master, so we have to drop your friends off. But we will make sure they're safe.

I'll try. Just don't make me angry. I may not be able to control myself.

CHAPTER 7

ON THE TRAIL

Back in Xenos, Wolfie and Xander are setting off to find Phoenix.

A wolf is a funny thing to bring on an adventure, too.

A book is a funny thing to bring on an adventure.

That's a good point, actually.

Besides, this book is all I need.

Is it magic? It doesn't smell like magic.

Magic has a smell?

Everything has a smell. Even you.

Don't worry. You smell fine.

Wait, I've picked up Phoenix's scent.

It says here that we should be careful not to fall into lava, and there are lots of zombie pigmen here.

Looks like Phoenix took care of a few here already.

So what's in there that I can't find out here in the real world?

This is the Book of Crafting. It tells you how to make ANYTHING.

Anything?

Try it out. Name something.

A comfy bed comes to mind.

Three wool and three wood planks. Coming right up!

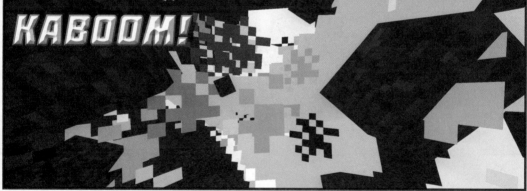

Meanwhile, back in Phoenix's village...

We have come to petition you on behalf of Phoenix, the outsider.

An outsider may not live within our gates. You know the rules, Ole Baba.

She lived among us for years before you knew she was not one of us.

We could have put you in jail for bringing her here.

Phoenix would have died if we left her all alone on that world.

Our world is not completely closed off, as you would like people to believe.

Like it or not, we are not alone. We should stop acting like we are.

It is time to stop being afraid of the outside world.

CHAPTER 8

THE PIRATE CAVE

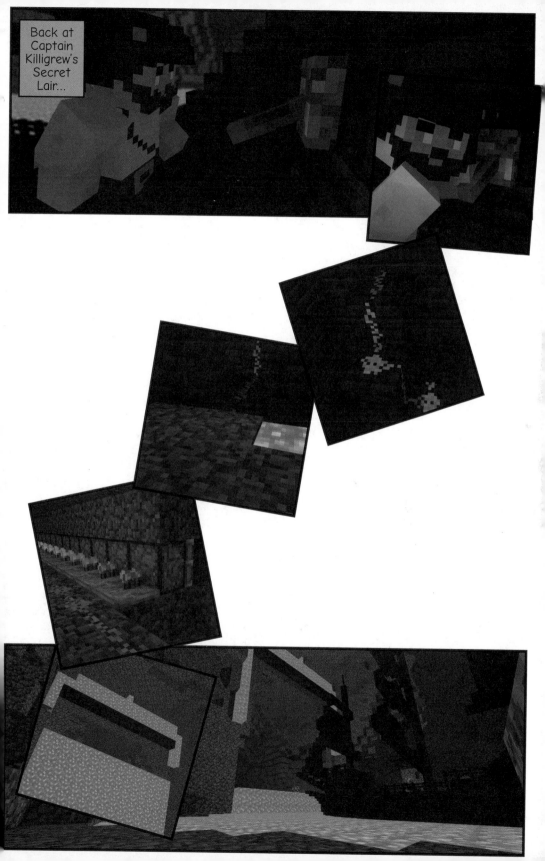

Back at Captain Killigrew's Secret Lair...

WHAP!

SQUEAL!

Oh no! Igor!

Oh Igor! Don't go to pieces on me now!

Come on, you lazy bones. Hop to it and dock this filthy barge.

⸘Oink!⸘

Aye, Captain!

Yes, sir!

Right away, sir!

Okie dokie!

Where are we?

Sigh. Captain Killigrew calls it Pirate's Cove. I call it The Nether Pits. If the lava smell doesn't get to you, the heat will.

Not that way. This way!

So why do you work for him if you hate it so much?

We owe him our lives.

Never mind. I'll do it myself.

He doesn't seem like the kind of guy who would save anyone.

I once lived in the Overworld, like you. But zombie pigmen aren't like other mobs. We are outcasts wherever we go.

More tea?

GROAN

We lived a peaceful life, and we thought we were safe.

Yes, please.

MOAN

BANG

CRASH

GROOOOAN

GRRR

AAAAAAHHHHH REEEE!

One day, zombies found a way to break through our iron door. We were defenseless!

Stand back! I'll save you!

Good thing I was here to protect you.

You saved our lives!

How can we ever repay you?

We followed the Captain to the Nether, and we've been working for him ever since.

Zombies can't go through an iron door on their own, you know.

Is it possible the Captain let them in?

!!!

Welcome to Pirate's Cove. Let's have a little chat, shall we?

You've heard that Concordia is a bit of a mess. That's good. The mess is what keeps people working hard.

You cheated!

You ruined my harvest!

You stole my wool!

Get off me!

You know why it's such a beautiful mess?

ME!

I run a very successful griefing business. If one farmer suspects another farmer of stealing his water, I help him get revenge.

They used to rely on me. I'd get paid twice for every fight.

If the other farmer gets griefed, guess who he calls to get that first guy back!

You are the cause of all their problems!

No, sweet, innocent girl. They had problems long before me.

But then some silly miner found a scroll that predicted a girl child with hair the color of apples would bring peace.

Those silly people were filled with hope. They stopped hiring me. They stopped arguing.

No one wanted to grief anyone anymore!

And that's a bad thing?

SCREEEEEE!

Come on. Let's get those messengers.

Let's take him to the dungeon.

At least give me my hat back!

We can start our bakery now!

That's a wonderful idea!

He's safely locked up, Miss Phoenix!

And we'll be here to guard him! We're going to start our own bakery!

NETHER CAKES sweet treats for all!

I was hoping this would happen someday. I even made a sign!

Good luck!

CHAPTER 9

REUNITED

Leaving those sprouts for me was a bright idea, sis.

It was the only way I could think of to leave a clue.

I was just lucky it was my little brother who came to get me. No one else would have found me so quickly.

Wait, how did you leave the village? Did you run away?

Would you believe they let me go? I've been training with Ole Baba since you left.

You took off with strangers by yourself. T.H. and his parents were worried.

But why did you go after me? How did you...

Oh! I'm sorry I made everyone worry.

Those are the messengers!

HI GUYS!

They're right where I left them.

Are you okay?

Oh yes, we've been passing the time quite nicely, chatting away.

Maybe Len's okay, but I can't listen to another second of his chatter. Get me off this island!

How did you dispatch Toby Killigrew and his dastardly zombie crew?

The crew was actually pretty nice. We got rid of the captain with help from my brother and pet wolf. The zombie pigman pirates set up a bakery. Here--have a cake!

Len, Squiq, I'd like to introduce you to my brother, Xander, and my loyal companion, Wolfie! They're the bravest guys I know!

Pleasure to meet you, Xander.

It's my pleasure, too. Nice to see you again, Wolfie.

It is quite a nice ship without the pirates and the threat of danger.

Those zombie pigman pirates are quite good bakers!

So, is my sister really a Profiteer?

You mean Prophetess? Yes. She fits the description perfectly.

This is all so strange to me. You've just always been my sister.

I'll always be your sister, but I have to know more about where I came from.

I know you have a past that we don't know about. And if you want to find out where you came from, then I'll be right here with you to help.

Thanks, Xan. It means a lot to me. I've missed you so much!

Where is Concordia? Why haven't I read about it in any books?

Concordia is not so much a town or village as a collection of miners who trade and work together. A community. no laws, no rulers.

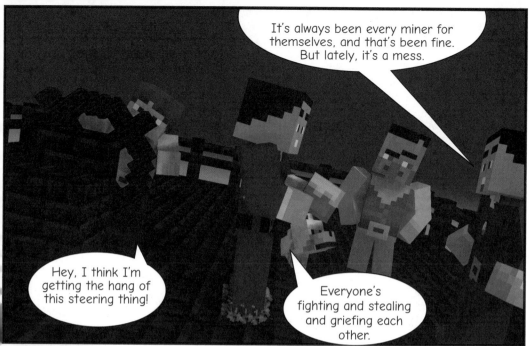

It's always been every miner for themselves, and that's been fine. But lately, it's a mess.

Hey, I think I'm getting the hang of this steering thing!

Everyone's fighting and stealing and griefing each other.

Do you really think my sister can help you?

Boy, sis, they really believe this prophecy stuff. You think you're the real thing?

≥Sniff≤

We hope so. She's our last hope.

We discovered a message that told of a young girl who meets your sister's description. I don't know how, but she will save us all!

Do you?

Because even if I could save them, I have no idea how I'd do it, you know?

Maybe having them believe in you is enough. Their problem is they disagree about everything...

If they all agree that you have the answers, they'll do whatever you tell them is right.

It would help people believe you if the necklace could start glowing again.

You planned this all along, didn't you?

Not the part where Toby became a pirate and kidnapped us. Or where the little brother showed up. But the fortress...well, yeah.

I can't fight you on this. Make it quick. And be safe.

Hooray!

Oh, man! More lava.

Just what I need for my potions.

You're big on potions.

Oh yes. I'm an alchemist when I'm not being a messenger. That's like a potion master. Len is a fisherman.

That certainly explains a lot about you.

Um, guys? You'd better come see this!

Is this Concordia?

Sniff, smells safe enough.

All safe and accounted for?

We're as close as we can get. The portal can't be too close to the community, or it could be dangerous.

What is that thing?

It's a real beacon, isn't it? I've seen one in my book.

Did someone say bacon?

The Nether drains us a bit, so we like to freshen up before we go to Concordia.

A little strength and regeneration, if you please, Squig.

CHAPTER 10

THE
PROPHETESS

Hang on a second...

Look, I'm just a kid. But if your stories say I'm going to come here and save you with my amulet, maybe you'd better tell me a little more...

...because I have no idea what I'm doing here.

There's not much to tell. A guy found a letter in a chest in an abandoned hut.

I heard he found it when he was cleaning a furnace.

Wherever he found it, it told the story of a girl who could help us.

Yeah. Then Traveling Max came back and said he saw a girl that fit the description when he was scavenging up at the monastery.

Traveling Max?

Thank you, everyone. But really, I can't accept these gifts. I have nowhere to put them, and no way to get them home.

Pssst! Phoenix, over here!

Excuse me everyone.

Phoenix, this is Brandor. He's the one who found the prophecy.

This is the letter I found. It was in an abandoned hut.

We are villagers on a mission to battle the Dragon. If you are reading this, we have failed. Please find our daughter, Violet. You will know her by an enchanted Ender eye necklace, hair the color of apples, and a tiny nose. She is in Elysia with friends. Please take care of our precious girl, and love her as we do. She will protect you and bring peace.

– Flora and Drake

Unfortunately, Elysia was destroyed in an invasion. We heard there were no survivors. But I guess there was one.

Me! But I guess my parents' friends didn't make it...

I had parents.

Parents who loved you.

Now you know where you came from.

I'm glad you're my family.

They say that about you, too!

Mom and Dad always said you were something special.

We have to get home to tell Mom and Dad!

Thank you for everything, but we have to go home now.

Thank *you* for everything. We owe you so much.

Please accept these Elytra in thanks. They will get get you home safely.

What do they do?

They're flying capes. We can fly home!

To use them, climb up really high, throw yourself at the ground...and miss!

That sounds easy...and scary!

Here's an interesting fact: Elytra don't help you fly--just glide.

As a final thank you, I would like to enchant them so you can fly instead of gliding.

GRUMBLE

Are you hungry, Little Brother?

We should stop soon. I'm hungry, too. I wish I had a zombie pigman cake!

It was nice of the miners to pack us such a great dinner!

They were grateful. I'm glad I could help them.

Everything looks tasty!

NOM NOM NOM.

Do you hear something?
No, just your loud chewing noises.
Wait. I do hear something. It's coming from over there.
It sounds like music. And laughter.
I guess we'll just follow the sparkles and see where they lead.
They haven't steered us wrong yet.

CHAPTER 11

SUPER FUN LAND

MOOOO
Did you just hear a "moo"?
It doesn't feel safe. I'm going to check my book.
Why doesn't it feel safe?
Because, so far, nothing we've done since we left the village has been completely safe.
Good point, little brother. What does the book say?
It says we're about to have FUN!

That was fun, but I have never been so tired! We need to make our beds and set up camp.

Excuse us, but we are sleepy and far from home. Can we use some of your wool?

Of course, child. Sweet dreams! ⸲Baaa⸲

This looks like a safe place to stop for the night.

You mean we're sleeping outdoors?

No, silly. We can make a house. Start digging.

Where'd you learn to do all this?

I learned a lot from T.H. when we were traveling together.

There has to be something here that tells how to ward off hostile mobs while we sleep.

Aha! We'll set a TNT trap outside the door with a redstone switch so we can turn it off when we wake up.

Nice! What would I do without my smart little brother?

Sweet dreams, Phoenix.

You, too, Xander.

When I was little, I used to dream I could fly. Like we did today with the Elytra.

What do you dream about, Phoenix?

What do you usually dream about?

I have the same dream every night: I have all the supplies I need, I never get hungry or hurt and can walk right past a hostile and never get attacked. I call my dream place **Creative mode**.

Okay, so that was weird. Care to explain?

It's a long story. Basically, she's the one who kidnapped me when you became a zombie.

So you befriended her?

I told you it's a long story. We've kind of helped each other out since then.

I can't even imagine the adventures you've had since you left home.

That's right! I did do all that. And I even lived to tell the tale.

I bet you can. You're the one who braved the Nether to rescue me from pirates, ended up as blaze bait, and flew across the Overworld on enchanted wings.

Unfortunately, the Elytra are almost spent, and it's uphill most of the way home.

Okay, sparkles. Do your stuff. Show us the way home!

I'm excited to go home, but sad to leave you.

But now that we know I'm really a villager, I'm a step closer to going home.

Poor thing, are you trapped?

I never thought of it that way, but I do feel trapped. Good point.

Oh, you meant the bunny.

There you go, little bunny. Hop on home!

The thing is, the only thing stopping me from going home is the villagers.

Mom and Dad and Ole Baba are working on them. They went to talk with the master librarians when you left.

I've done everything I could, but to them I'm still the kid that got you turned into a zombie.

Yeah, that was definitely the low point in my life so far.

Sorry about that. My bad.

Nah. Don't worry. It probably would've happened eventually.

CHAPTER 12

SURPRISE

≈Cluck?≈ You're looking for Wolfie? He had to go back with his family.

I'll miss that pup.

Did you get hurt? Where are those messengers? What happened?

I'd like to hear you tell it, because if I hadn't lived through it, I wouldn't believe any of it.

NETHER CANES sweet treats for all!!

How did you get out of the village?

Moosha caused a distraction, and we all slipped out without being noticed.

We wanted so much to come see you.

We have the proof we need to get Phoenix home.

That's wonderful news! We have been working with the elders to consider opening the town gates for trade.

A zombie pigman in a chef's hat delivered this cart for you before dawn this morning.

To Phoenix, Xander and Wolfie, with love from the zombie pigman pirates of Nether Cakes

To Phoenix and Xander's safe return!